fourth day of Christ - mas my true love sent to me, Four coll - y birds,

three French hens, two tur - tle doves and a par - tridge in a pear

tree.___ The fifth day of Christ - mas my true love sent to me,

Five gold___ rings, Four coll - y birds, three French hens,

two___ tur - tle doves and a par - tridge in a pear tree. *etc.*

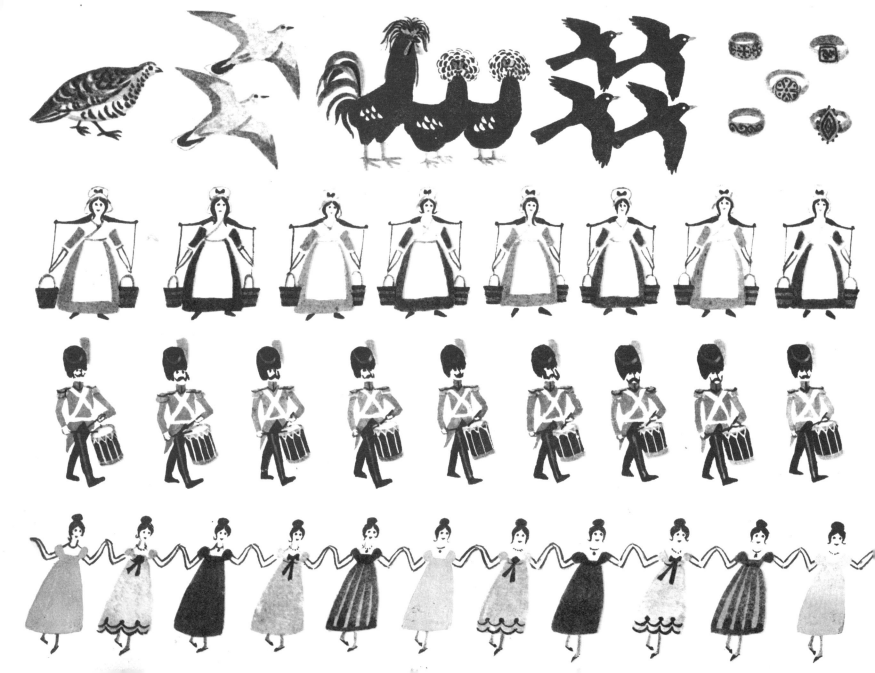

The Twelve Days of Christmas

A picture book by Robert Broomfield

THE BODLEY HEAD · LONDON · SYDNEY · TORONTO

The first day of Christmas
My true love sent to me
A partridge in a pear tree.

The second day of Christmas
My true love sent to me
Two turtle doves, and
A partridge in a pear tree.

The third day of Christmas
My true love sent to me
Three French hens,
Two turtle doves, and
A partridge in a pear tree.

The fourth day of Christmas
My true love sent to me
Four colly birds,
Three French hens,
Two turtle doves, and
A partridge in a pear tree.

The fifth day of Christmas
My true love sent to me
Five gold rings,
Four colly birds,
Three French hens,
Two turtle doves, and
A partridge in a pear tree.

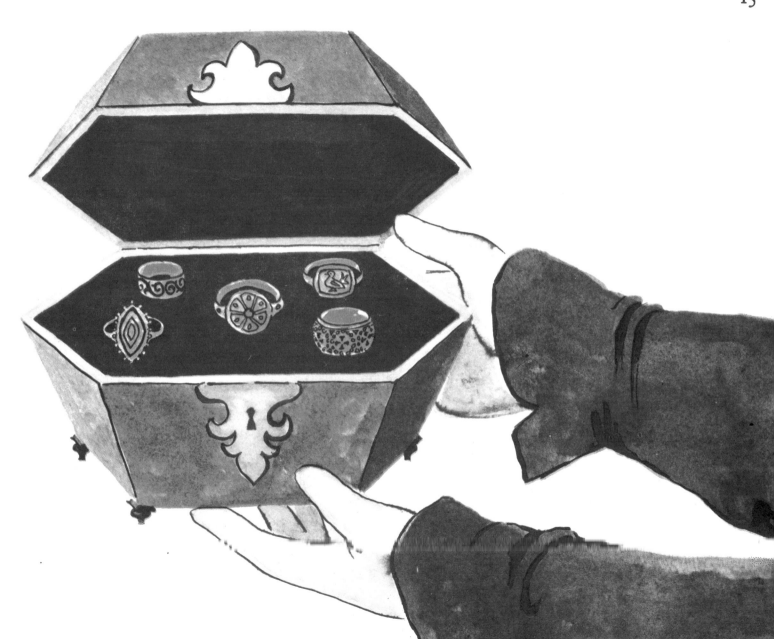

The sixth day of Christmas
My true love sent to me
Six geese a-laying,
Five gold rings,
Four colly birds,
Three French hens,
Two turtle doves, and
A partridge in a pear tree.

The seventh day of Christmas
My true love sent to me
Seven swans a-swimming,
Six geese a-laying,
Five gold rings,
Four colly birds,
Three French hens,
Two turtle doves, and
A partridge in a pear tree.

The eighth day of Christmas
My true love sent to me
Eight maids a-milking,
Seven swans a-swimming,
Six geese a-laying,
Five gold rings,
Four colly birds,
Three French hens,
Two turtle doves, and
A partridge in a pear tree.

The ninth day of Christmas
My true love sent to me
Nine drummers drumming,
Eight maids a-milking,
Seven swans a-swimming,
Six geese a-laying,
Five gold rings,
Four colly birds,
Three French hens,
Two turtle doves, and
A partridge in a pear tree.

The tenth day of Christmas
My true love sent to me
Ten pipers piping,
Nine drummers drumming,
Eight maids a-milking,
Seven swans a-swimming,
Six geese a-laying,
Five gold rings,
Four colly birds,
Three French hens,
Two turtle doves, and
A partridge in a pear tree.

The eleventh day of Christmas
My true love sent to me
Eleven ladies dancing,
Ten pipers piping,
Nine drummers drumming,
Eight maids a-milking,
Seven swans a-swimming,
Six geese a-laying,
Five gold rings,
Four colly birds,
Three French hens,
Two turtle doves, and
A partridge in a pear tree.

The twelfth day of Christmas
My true love sent to me
Twelve lords a-leaping,
Eleven ladies dancing,
Ten pipers piping,
Nine drummers drumming,
Eight maids a-milking,
Seven swans a-swimming,
Six geese a-laying,
Five gold rings,
Four colly birds,
Three French hens,
Two turtle doves, and
A partridge in a pear tree.

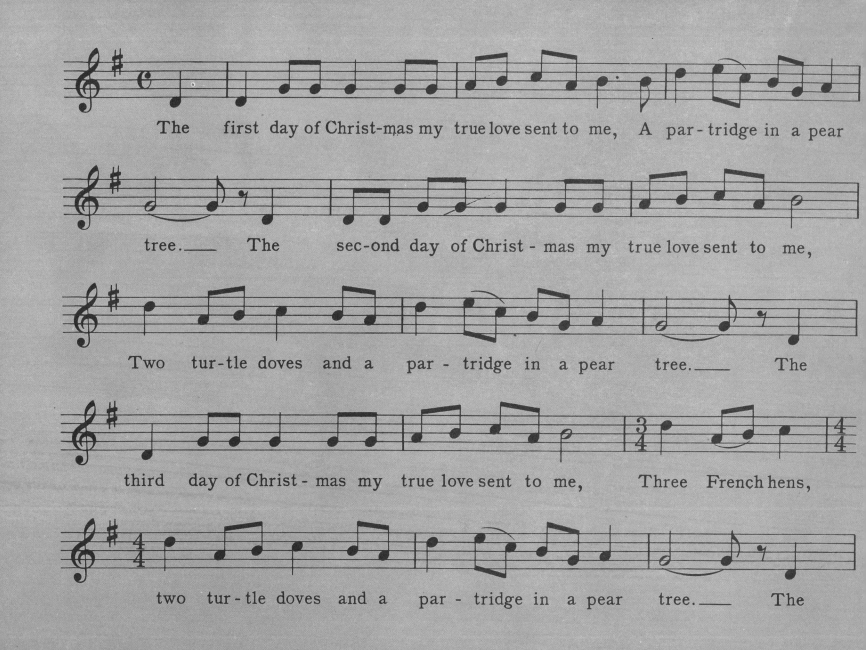

The   first day of Christ-mas my true love sent to me,   A par - tridge in a pear

tree.___   The   sec-ond day of Christ - mas my   true love sent to me,

Two   tur-tle doves and a   par - tridge in a pear   tree.___   The

third   day of Christ - mas my   true love sent to me,   Three French hens,

two   tur - tle doves and a   par - tridge in a pear   tree.___   The

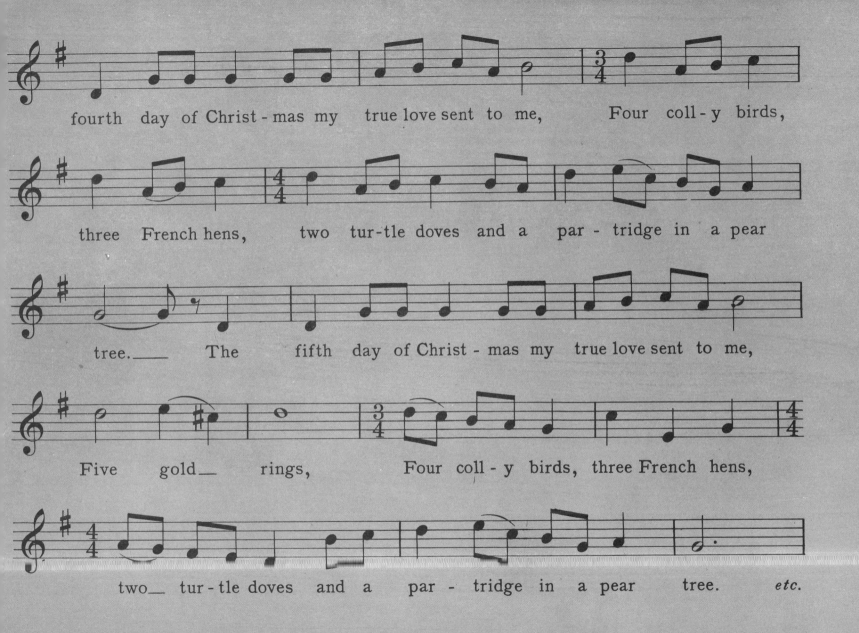

fourth day of Christ - mas my true love sent to me, Four coll - y birds,

three French hens, two tur-tle doves and a par - tridge in a pear

tree.____ The fifth day of Christ - mas my true love sent to me,

Five gold__ rings, Four coll - y birds, three French hens,

two__ tur-tle doves and a par - tridge in a pear tree. *etc.*

ISBN 0 370 00750 6
All rights reserved
Illustrations © The Bodley Head Ltd 1965
Printed in Great Britain for
The Bodley Head Ltd
9 Bow Street, London WC2E 7AL
by A. & M. Weston Ltd, South Wigston, Leicestershire
First published 1965
Reprinted 1967, 1971